Monster Mount

Written by Adam and Charlotte Guillain

Rav and Finn were spending the day at the Planet Zoom theme park.

The two friends made their way to the start. They could hear roaring sounds coming from inside.

"It looks a bit dark," muttered Finn.

"Come on," called Rav. "I've got a whistle in case we get lost!"

They couldn't see anyone else inside the maze, and the high walls threw down long, dark shadows. At the next turning, Finn heard a growling noise.

"This way," he whispered, heading in the opposite direction.

As the pathway curved round to the right, the boys stopped in their tracks. A shadow was moving towards them with outstretched arms!

"Run!" shouted Rav.

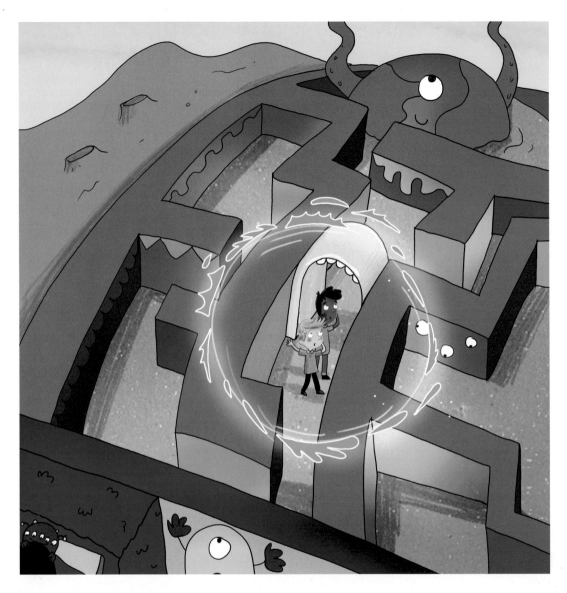

They sprinted down another path and through an archway. The ground beneath their feet began to shudder like a washing machine.

"What now?" hissed Finn.

When the shaking stopped, bright light hit their faces. They were no longer in the maze, but looked out at a rocky landscape.

"We're on a mountain," said Rav, his eyes wide.

"I think we're on another planet!" cried Finn.

They turned around and found that the archway back to Planet Zoom had vanished.

"How will we get back now?" asked Finn, his hands shaking.

Rav looked around. "There's another archway up the slope!" he cried. "Come on."

They headed up the slope towards some strange, alien plants with slimy, pink leaves. They stopped in their tracks as a shrill howl shattered the silence.

"W-what's that?" stammered Rav.

"Something's moving over there!" whispered Finn.

The boys froze as a massive, yellow monster emerged from behind a plant. It towered above them and opened its jaws to howl again. Then it spotted Rav and Finn.

"Oh, phew!" sighed the monster. "I thought you were that big monster from up the mountain, but you don't look scary at all!"

Rav and Finn unfroze, smiled and introduced themselves.

We're from planet Earth.

The monster glanced up the mountain. "Be careful if you're heading up there," it said. "You don't want that big brute to eat you. Why don't you stay safe here? I get lonely on my own."

Finn gulped. "We have to go up there to get back to our planet," he said.

The monster sighed and hid behind the plant.

The boys hadn't trudged much further when they spotted gigantic footprints.

Something purple and scaly jumped out on the path ahead, holding up its claws! Finn grabbed Rav and croaked, "Run!"

"Oh," said the monster. "I thought you were that fearsome, furry monster from down there. I'm afraid it will come up and eat me."

"That monster's not scary!" said Finn.

But the purple monster was too busy wailing to hear Finn. The boys walked on up the mountain.

"Watch out! There are more monstrous creatures up there!" shrieked the monster.

"We're nearly at the archway," puffed Rav, as they strode on up the path. Just in front of the arch, they had to cross some soft, blue moss.

"The ground's moving," said Rav. "We must be going back already."

"No, we're not!" shouted Finn. "Look!"

"More monsters!" yelled Rav.

The little, blue monsters looked up at them and screamed!

Rav and Finn watched with their mouths open as the blue monsters rolled away down the slope.

"Don't be afraid of us!" cried Finn.

They ran after the screaming monsters, waving and shouting.

As the blue monsters rolled through the rocks,
the purple, scaly monster jumped out. It held up its
arms, shrieked and ran down the mountain, followed
by the little, blue monsters and the boys.

A horrible howl echoed around as the furry, yellow monster spotted the other monsters hurtling down the mountain towards it. It started to run in circles.

Rav blew his whistle. All the monsters stopped and stared at him.

"They're going to eat me!" whimpered all the monsters.

"Is that true?" asked Finn.

"I only eat plants," mumbled the furry, yellow monster.

"Me too!" cried all the others.

The monsters quickly realised that they didn't need to be scared. As they made friends, Finn and Rav headed back up the slope to the archway. They ducked through it and the ground began to shake.

Back in the maze, Finn and Rav weren't scared. They ran around the corners and laughed at the funny monsters that jumped out and roared. Soon they had reached the middle.

Talk about the story

Answer the questions:

1 What was the maze called?

2 What sort of monster did the boys meet first?

3 What did the purple monster think the yellow monster would do to him?

4 What does the word 'strode' mean? Can you think of another word that means the same thing?

5 Why do you think the little, blue monsters were afraid of Rav and Finn?

6 Why did the monsters make friends at the end?

7 Can you describe all the different monsters that Rav and Finn met on Monster Mountain?

8 Have you ever been in a maze? Did you find the middle/the way out?

Can you retell the story in your own words?